Recipe Collector
and Journal

"Many are the ways and many the recipes ..."
Archestratus

The Recipe Collector and Journal is ideal for storing all of your favourite recipes. This practical book is divided into easily manageable sections. Each section includes pages for you to record your own recipes, or those handed down or passed on by friends.
The pages allow you to clearly record the name of the recipe, how many the recipe will serve and how long the recipe takes to prepare and to cook.

There is also a "Difficulty Rating" where you can easily identify the complexity of the recipe by circling the relevant number. The scale runs from one to five and should be circled or crossed through in ascending order of difficulty, with "one" being relatively easy and "five" being for those recipes that require more skill or attention. This scale creates an invaluable reference tool - if you are looking for a quick and easy recipe for say unexpected visitors, or if you are teaching others to cook they can work their way through the scale.

In addition, each section also includes a series of pages where you can affix recipes cut out from magazines and newspapers.

The first divider also doubles as a keepsake pocket where it is possible to store any recipe cards you may have. In this pocket you will find a pack of Magic Dots™ mounts.

Peel back the protective wax paper to access the dots and then pick up the dots by pressing the back of your recipe cutting firmly onto a dot. Place one dot in each corner of the cutting and then press this onto the required page in the journal. Please note that for storage, the waxed backing paper should be replaced over the dots shiny-side down.

Basic conversion tables

Heat level	Fahrenheit	Centigrade	Gas Mark
Very cool	200	95	0
Very cool	225	110	1/4
Very cool	250	120	1/2
Cool or slow	275	135	1
Cool or slow	300	150	2
Warm	325	165	3
Moderate	350	175	4
Moderately hot	375	190	5
Fairly hot	400	200	6
Hot	425	220	7
Very Hot	450	230	8
Very Hot	475	245	9

Approximate Metric Equivalents by Weight

Imperial.	Metric.
1/4 ounce	7 grams
1/2 ounce	14 grams
1 ounce	28 grams
1 1/4 ounces	35 grams
1 1/2 ounces	40 grams
2 1/2 ounces	70 grams
4 ounces	112 grams
5 ounces	140 grams
8 ounces	228 grams
10 ounces	280 grams
15 ounces	425 grams
16 ounces (1lb)	454 grams

Metric.	Imperial.
1 gram	0.035 ounce
50 grams	1.75 ounces
100 grams	3.5 ounces
250 grams	8.75 ounces
500 grams	1.1 pounds
1 kilogram	2.2 pounds

Substitutes for herbs and spices

Basil	Oregano or thyme
Chervil	Tarragon or parsley
Chive	Spring onion; onion; or leek
Coriander	Parsley
Italian Seasoning	Blend of any of these: basil, oregano, rosemary, and ground red pepper
Marjoram	Basil or thyme
Mint	Basil; marjoram; or rosemary
Oregano	Thyme or basil
Parsley	Chervil or coriander
Poultry Seasoning	Sage plus a blend of any of these: thyme, marjoram, savory, black pepper, and rosemary
Red Pepper	Dash bottled hot pepper sauce or black pepper
Rosemary	Thyme or tarragon
Sage	Poultry seasoning; marjoram; or rosemary
Savory	Thyme; marjoram; or sage
Tarragon	Chervil; fennel seed; or aniseed
Thyme	Basil; marjoram; or oregano
Allspice	Cinnamon; cassia; dash of nutmeg or mace; or dash of cloves
Aniseed	Fennel seed or a few drops of anise extract
Cardamom	Ginger
Chili Powder	Dash bottled hot pepper sauce plus a combination of oregano and cumin
Cinnamon	Nutmeg or allspice (use only 1/4 of the amount)
Cloves	Allspice; cinnamon; or nutmeg
Cumin	Chili powder
Ginger	Allspice; cinnamon; mace; or nutmeg
Mace	Allspice; cinnamon; ginger; or nutmeg
Nutmeg	Cinnamon; ginger; or mace
Saffron	Dash turmeric (for colour)

starters and snacks

Recipe --

Serves _____ Preparation time _____

Difficulty Scale [1] [2] [3] [4] [5]   Cooking time _____

Ingredients

Name   Weight/Measure/Amount

-- --

-- --

-- --

-- --

-- --

-- --

-- --

Method

Recipe --

Serves _____ Preparation time _____

Difficulty Scale [1|2|3|4|5] Cooking time _____

Ingredients

Name	Weight/Measure/Amount
----------------------------------	----------------------------------
----------------------------------	----------------------------------
----------------------------------	----------------------------------
----------------------------------	----------------------------------
----------------------------------	----------------------------------
----------------------------------	----------------------------------
----------------------------------	----------------------------------

Method

Recipe --

Serves _____ Preparation time _____

Difficulty Scale | 1 | 2 | 3 | 4 | 5 | Cooking time   _____

Ingredients

Name	Weight/Measure/Amount
---------------------------	---------------------------
---------------------------	---------------------------
---------------------------	---------------------------
---------------------------	---------------------------
---------------------------	---------------------------
---------------------------	---------------------------
---------------------------	---------------------------

Method

Recipe

Serves _____   Preparation time _____

Difficulty Scale | 1 | 2 | 3 | 4 | 5 | Cooking time _____

Ingredients

Name   Weight/Measure/Amount

------------------------------   ------------------------------

------------------------------   ------------------------------

------------------------------   ------------------------------

------------------------------   ------------------------------

------------------------------   ------------------------------

------------------------------   ------------------------------

------------------------------   ------------------------------

Method

Recipe --

Serves _____ Preparation time _____

Difficulty Scale | 1 | 2 | 3 | 4 | 5 | Cooking time _____

Ingredients

Name	Weight/Measure/Amount
----------------------------------	----------------------------------
----------------------------------	----------------------------------
----------------------------------	----------------------------------
----------------------------------	----------------------------------
----------------------------------	----------------------------------
----------------------------------	----------------------------------
----------------------------------	----------------------------------

Method

Recipe --

Serves _____   Preparation time _____

Difficulty Scale [1][2][3][4][5]   Cooking time _____

Ingredients

Name   Weight/Measure/Amount

--------------------------------   --------------------------------

--------------------------------   --------------------------------

--------------------------------   --------------------------------

--------------------------------   --------------------------------

--------------------------------   --------------------------------

--------------------------------   --------------------------------

--------------------------------   --------------------------------

Method

Recipe --

Serves _____ Preparation time _____

Difficulty Scale [1] [2] [3] [4] [5]   Cooking time _____

Ingredients

Name   Weight/Measure/Amount

-- --
-- --
-- --
-- --
-- --
-- --
-- --

Method

Recipe --

Serves _____ Preparation time _____

Difficulty Scale [1][2][3][4][5] Cooking time _____

Ingredients

Name   Weight/Measure/Amount

---------------------------------   ---------------------------------

---------------------------------   ---------------------------------

---------------------------------   ---------------------------------

---------------------------------   ---------------------------------

---------------------------------   ---------------------------------

---------------------------------   ---------------------------------

---------------------------------   ---------------------------------

Method

Recipe ....

Serves _____   Preparation time _____

Difficulty Scale | 1 | 2 | 3 | 4 | 5 | Cooking time _____

Ingredients

Name	Weight/Measure/Amount
----------------------------------	----------------------------------
----------------------------------	----------------------------------
----------------------------------	----------------------------------
----------------------------------	----------------------------------
----------------------------------	----------------------------------
----------------------------------	----------------------------------
----------------------------------	----------------------------------

Method

Recipe ....

Serves _____ Preparation time _____

Difficulty Scale | 1 | 2 | 3 | 4 | 5 | Cooking time _____

Ingredients

Name	Weight/Measure/Amount
-------------------------------	-------------------------------
-------------------------------	-------------------------------
-------------------------------	-------------------------------
-------------------------------	-------------------------------
-------------------------------	-------------------------------
-------------------------------	-------------------------------
-------------------------------	-------------------------------

Method

----

place recipes here

place recipes here

salads, stir-fries and pasta

Recipe ....

Serves _____   Preparation time _____

Difficulty Scale | 1 | 2 | 3 | 4 | 5 | Cooking time _____

Ingredients

Name	Weight/Measure/Amount
------------------------------	------------------------------
------------------------------	------------------------------
------------------------------	------------------------------
------------------------------	------------------------------
------------------------------	------------------------------
------------------------------	------------------------------
------------------------------	------------------------------

Method

Recipe --

Serves _____ Preparation time _____

Difficulty Scale [1][2][3][4][5] Cooking time _____

Ingredients

Name	Weight/Measure/Amount
-------------------------------	-------------------------------
-------------------------------	-------------------------------
-------------------------------	-------------------------------
-------------------------------	-------------------------------
-------------------------------	-------------------------------
-------------------------------	-------------------------------
-------------------------------	-------------------------------

Method

Recipe --

Serves _____   Preparation time _____

Difficulty Scale | 1 | 2 | 3 | 4 | 5 | Cooking time   _____

Ingredients

Name   Weight/Measure/Amount

-----------------------------------   -----------------------------------

-----------------------------------   -----------------------------------

-----------------------------------   -----------------------------------

-----------------------------------   -----------------------------------

-----------------------------------   -----------------------------------

-----------------------------------   -----------------------------------

-----------------------------------   -----------------------------------

Method

Recipe --

Serves _____ Preparation time _____

Difficulty Scale | 1 | 2 | 3 | 4 | 5 | Cooking time   _____

Ingredients

Name   Weight/Measure/Amount

--------------------------------   --------------------------------

--------------------------------   --------------------------------

--------------------------------   --------------------------------

--------------------------------   --------------------------------

--------------------------------   --------------------------------

--------------------------------   --------------------------------

--------------------------------   --------------------------------

Method

Recipe --

Serves _____   Preparation time _____

Difficulty Scale   [1] [2] [3] [4] [5]   Cooking time   _____

Ingredients

Name	Weight/Measure/Amount
------------------------------	------------------------------
------------------------------	------------------------------
------------------------------	------------------------------
------------------------------	------------------------------
------------------------------	------------------------------
------------------------------	------------------------------
------------------------------	------------------------------

Method

Recipe --

Serves _____ Preparation time _____

Difficulty Scale   1 2 3 4 5   Cooking time _____

Ingredients

Name   Weight/Measure/Amount

----------------------------------   ----------------------------------

----------------------------------   ----------------------------------

----------------------------------   ----------------------------------

----------------------------------   ----------------------------------

----------------------------------   ----------------------------------

----------------------------------   ----------------------------------

----------------------------------   ----------------------------------

Method

Recipe

Serves _____   Preparation time _____

Difficulty Scale [1][2][3][4][5]   Cooking time _____

Ingredients

Name   Weight/Measure/Amount

----------------------------------   ----------------------------------

----------------------------------   ----------------------------------

----------------------------------   ----------------------------------

----------------------------------   ----------------------------------

----------------------------------   ----------------------------------

----------------------------------   ----------------------------------

----------------------------------   ----------------------------------

Method

Recipe

Serves _____ Preparation time _____

Difficulty Scale [1] [2] [3] [4] [5] Cooking time _____

Ingredients

Name	Weight/Measure/Amount
-------------------------------	-------------------------------
-------------------------------	-------------------------------
-------------------------------	-------------------------------
-------------------------------	-------------------------------
-------------------------------	-------------------------------
-------------------------------	-------------------------------
-------------------------------	-------------------------------

Method

Recipe ....

Serves _____ Preparation time _____

Difficulty Scale | 1 | 2 | 3 | 4 | 5 | Cooking time _____

Ingredients

Name   Weight/Measure/Amount

------------------------------------   ------------------------------------
------------------------------------   ------------------------------------
------------------------------------   ------------------------------------
------------------------------------   ------------------------------------
------------------------------------   ------------------------------------
------------------------------------   ------------------------------------
------------------------------------   ------------------------------------

Method

Recipe

Serves _____   Preparation time _____

Difficulty Scale | 1 | 2 | 3 | 4 | 5 | Cooking time _____

Ingredients

Name	Weight/Measure/Amount
------------------------------	------------------------------
------------------------------	------------------------------
------------------------------	------------------------------
------------------------------	------------------------------
------------------------------	------------------------------
------------------------------	------------------------------
------------------------------	------------------------------

Method

----

place recipes here

place recipes here

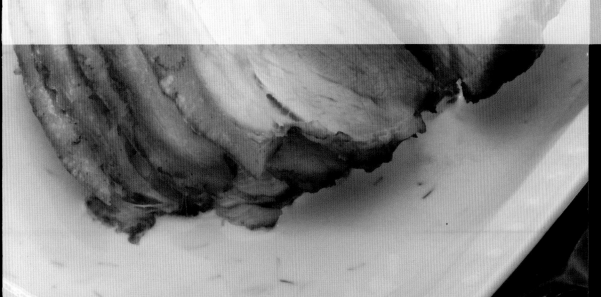

meat, fish and poultry

Recipe --

Serves _____   Preparation time _____

Difficulty Scale | 1 | 2 | 3 | 4 | 5 | Cooking time   _____

Ingredients

Name	Weight/Measure/Amount
------------------------------	------------------------------
------------------------------	------------------------------
------------------------------	------------------------------
------------------------------	------------------------------
------------------------------	------------------------------
------------------------------	------------------------------
------------------------------	------------------------------

Method

Recipe

Serves _____ Preparation time _____

Difficulty Scale [1] [2] [3] [4] [5]   Cooking time   _____

Ingredients

Name   Weight/Measure/Amount

------------------------------------   -------------------------------

------------------------------------   -------------------------------

------------------------------------   -------------------------------

------------------------------------   -------------------------------

------------------------------------   -------------------------------

------------------------------------   -------------------------------

------------------------------------   -------------------------------

Method

Recipe ....

Serves _____ Preparation time _____

Difficulty Scale | 1 | 2 | 3 | 4 | 5 | Cooking time _____

Ingredients

Name   Weight/Measure/Amount

--------------------------------   --------------------------------

--------------------------------   --------------------------------

--------------------------------   --------------------------------

--------------------------------   --------------------------------

--------------------------------   --------------------------------

--------------------------------   --------------------------------

--------------------------------   --------------------------------

Method

Recipe --

Serves _____ Preparation time _____

Difficulty Scale | 1 | 2 | 3 | 4 | 5 | Cooking time _____

Ingredients

Name   Weight/Measure/Amount

------------------------------------   ------------------------------------

------------------------------------   ------------------------------------

------------------------------------   ------------------------------------

------------------------------------   ------------------------------------

------------------------------------   ------------------------------------

------------------------------------   ------------------------------------

------------------------------------   ------------------------------------

Method

Recipe ---

Serves _____ Preparation time _____

Difficulty Scale | 1 | 2 | 3 | 4 | 5 | Cooking time _____

Ingredients

Name   Weight/Measure/Amount

------------------------------------   ------------------------------------

------------------------------------   ------------------------------------

------------------------------------   ------------------------------------

------------------------------------   ------------------------------------

------------------------------------   ------------------------------------

------------------------------------   ------------------------------------

------------------------------------   ------------------------------------

Method

Recipe

Serves _____ Preparation time _____

Difficulty Scale | 1 | 2 | 3 | 4 | 5 | Cooking time _____

Ingredients

Name	Weight/Measure/Amount
------------------------------	------------------------------
------------------------------	------------------------------
------------------------------	------------------------------
------------------------------	------------------------------
------------------------------	------------------------------
------------------------------	------------------------------
------------------------------	------------------------------

Method

Recipe

Serves _____ Preparation time _____

Difficulty Scale | 1 | 2 | 3 | 4 | 5 | Cooking time _____

Ingredients

Name   Weight/Measure/Amount

------------------------------   ------------------------------------

------------------------------   ------------------------------------

------------------------------   ------------------------------------

------------------------------   ------------------------------------

------------------------------   ------------------------------------

------------------------------   ------------------------------------

------------------------------   ------------------------------------

Method

Recipe ....

Serves _____   Preparation time _____

Difficulty Scale   [1] [2] [3] [4] [5]   Cooking time   _____

Ingredients

Name	Weight/Measure/Amount
-----	-----
-----	-----
-----	-----
-----	-----
-----	-----
-----	-----
-----	-----

Method

Recipe

Serves _____   Preparation time _____

Difficulty Scale | 1 | 2 | 3 | 4 | 5 | Cooking time _____

Ingredients

Name   Weight/Measure/Amount

-- --

-- --

-- --

-- --

-- --

-- --

-- --

Method

Recipe

Serves _____ Preparation time _____

Difficulty Scale [1] [2] [3] [4] [5]   Cooking time _____

Ingredients

Name   Weight/Measure/Amount

----------------------------------   ----------------------------------

----------------------------------   ----------------------------------

----------------------------------   ----------------------------------

----------------------------------   ----------------------------------

----------------------------------   ----------------------------------

----------------------------------   ----------------------------------

----------------------------------   ----------------------------------

Method

Recipe

Serves _____   Preparation time _____

Difficulty Scale | 1 | 2 | 3 | 4 | 5 | Cooking time _____

Ingredients

Name   Weight/Measure/Amount

------------------------------   ------------------------------

------------------------------   ------------------------------

------------------------------   ------------------------------

------------------------------   ------------------------------

------------------------------   ------------------------------

------------------------------   ------------------------------

------------------------------   ------------------------------

Method

Recipe ---

Serves _____ Preparation time _____

Difficulty Scale | 1 | 2 | 3 | 4 | 5 | Cooking time _____

Ingredients

Name   Weight/Measure/Amount

-------------------------------   -------------------------------

-------------------------------   -------------------------------

-------------------------------   -------------------------------

-------------------------------   -------------------------------

-------------------------------   -------------------------------

-------------------------------   -------------------------------

-------------------------------   -------------------------------

Method

Recipe

Serves _____ Preparation time _____

Difficulty Scale [1] [2] [3] [4] [5]   Cooking time _____

Ingredients

Name   Weight/Measure/Amount

--------------------------------   --------------------------------

--------------------------------   --------------------------------

--------------------------------   --------------------------------

--------------------------------   --------------------------------

--------------------------------   --------------------------------

--------------------------------   --------------------------------

--------------------------------   --------------------------------

Method

Recipe

Serves _____ Preparation time _____

Difficulty Scale [1][2][3][4][5] Cooking time _____

Ingredients

Name   Weight/Measure/Amount

------------------------------------   ------------------------------------

------------------------------------   ------------------------------------

------------------------------------   ------------------------------------

------------------------------------   ------------------------------------

------------------------------------   ------------------------------------

------------------------------------   ------------------------------------

------------------------------------   ------------------------------------

Method

----

place recipes here

place recipes here

place recipes here

place recipes here

vegetable dishes

Recipe --

Serves _____ Preparation time _____

Difficulty Scale | 1 | 2 | 3 | 4 | 5 | Cooking time _____

Ingredients

Name   Weight/Measure/Amount

--------------------------------   --------------------------------

--------------------------------   --------------------------------

--------------------------------   --------------------------------

--------------------------------   --------------------------------

--------------------------------   --------------------------------

--------------------------------   --------------------------------

--------------------------------   --------------------------------

Method

Recipe ....

Serves _____ Preparation time _____

Difficulty Scale | 1 | 2 | 3 | 4 | 5 | Cooking time _____

Ingredients

Name   Weight/Measure/Amount

-------------------------------------   -------------------------------------

-------------------------------------   -------------------------------------

-------------------------------------   -------------------------------------

-------------------------------------   -------------------------------------

-------------------------------------   -------------------------------------

-------------------------------------   -------------------------------------

-------------------------------------   -------------------------------------

Method

Recipe

Serves _____ Preparation time _____

Difficulty Scale [1] [2] [3] [4] [5]   Cooking time _____

Ingredients

Name   Weight/Measure/Amount

-----------------------------------   -----------------------------------

-----------------------------------   -----------------------------------

-----------------------------------   -----------------------------------

-----------------------------------   -----------------------------------

-----------------------------------   -----------------------------------

-----------------------------------   -----------------------------------

-----------------------------------   -----------------------------------

Method

Recipe

Serves _____   Preparation time _____

Difficulty Scale [1] [2] [3] [4] [5]   Cooking time _____

Ingredients

Name   Weight/Measure/Amount

------------------------------------   ------------------------------------

------------------------------------   ------------------------------------

------------------------------------   ------------------------------------

------------------------------------   ------------------------------------

------------------------------------   ------------------------------------

------------------------------------   ------------------------------------

------------------------------------   ------------------------------------

Method

Recipe

Serves _____ Preparation time _____

Difficulty Scale 1 2 3 4 5   Cooking time _____

Ingredients

Name   Weight/Measure/Amount

-------------------------------   -------------------------------

-------------------------------   -------------------------------

-------------------------------   -------------------------------

-------------------------------   -------------------------------

-------------------------------   -------------------------------

-------------------------------   -------------------------------

-------------------------------   -------------------------------

Method

Recipe --

Serves _____ Preparation time _____

Difficulty Scale | 1 | 2 | 3 | 4 | 5 | Cooking time _____

Ingredients

Name   Weight/Measure/Amount

------------------------------------   ------------------------------------
------------------------------------   ------------------------------------
------------------------------------   ------------------------------------
------------------------------------   ------------------------------------
------------------------------------   ------------------------------------
------------------------------------   ------------------------------------
------------------------------------   ------------------------------------

Method

Recipe

Serves _____ Preparation time _____

Difficulty Scale [1][2][3][4][5] Cooking time _____

Ingredients

Name   Weight/Measure/Amount

------------------------------------   ------------------------------------

------------------------------------   ------------------------------------

------------------------------------   ------------------------------------

------------------------------------   ------------------------------------

------------------------------------   ------------------------------------

------------------------------------   ------------------------------------

------------------------------------   ------------------------------------

Method

Recipe ....

Serves _____ Preparation time _____

Difficulty Scale | 1 | 2 | 3 | 4 | 5 | Cooking time _____

Ingredients

Name   Weight/Measure/Amount

-------------------------------------   -------------------------------------

-------------------------------------   -------------------------------------

-------------------------------------   -------------------------------------

-------------------------------------   -------------------------------------

-------------------------------------   -------------------------------------

-------------------------------------   -------------------------------------

-------------------------------------   -------------------------------------

Method

Recipe

Serves _____ Preparation time _____

Difficulty Scale | 1 | 2 | 3 | 4 | 5 | Cooking time   _____

Ingredients

Name	Weight/Measure/Amount
----------------------------	----------------------------
----------------------------	----------------------------
----------------------------	----------------------------
----------------------------	----------------------------
----------------------------	----------------------------
----------------------------	----------------------------
----------------------------	----------------------------

Method

Recipe --

Serves _____ Preparation time _____

Difficulty Scale | 1 | 2 | 3 | 4 | 5 | Cooking time _____

Ingredients

Name   Weight/Measure/Amount

-----------------------------------   -----------------------------------
-----------------------------------   -----------------------------------
-----------------------------------   -----------------------------------
-----------------------------------   -----------------------------------
-----------------------------------   -----------------------------------
-----------------------------------   -----------------------------------
-----------------------------------   -----------------------------------

Method

Recipe

Serves _____ Preparation time _____

Difficulty Scale [1] [2] [3] [4] [5]   Cooking time _____

Ingredients

Name	Weight/Measure/Amount

Method

Recipe

Serves _____   Preparation time _____

Difficulty Scale | 1 | 2 | 3 | 4 | 5 | Cooking time _____

Ingredients

Name	Weight/Measure/Amount
--------------------------	--------------------------
--------------------------	--------------------------
--------------------------	--------------------------
--------------------------	--------------------------
--------------------------	--------------------------
--------------------------	--------------------------
--------------------------	--------------------------

Method

Recipe

Serves _____ Preparation time _____

Difficulty Scale [1] [2] [3] [4] [5] Cooking time _____

Ingredients

Name   Weight/Measure/Amount

-------------------------------   -------------------------------

-------------------------------   -------------------------------

-------------------------------   -------------------------------

-------------------------------   -------------------------------

-------------------------------   -------------------------------

-------------------------------   -------------------------------

-------------------------------   -------------------------------

Method

Recipe _____

Serves _____ Preparation time _____

Difficulty Scale ⬚ 1 ⬚ 2 ⬚ 3 ⬚ 4 ⬚ 5 Cooking time _____

Ingredients

Name   Weight/Measure/Amount

--   --

--   --

--   --

--   --

--   --

--   --

--   --

Method

----

place recipes here

place recipes here

place recipes here

place recipes here

desserts

Recipe

Serves _____ Preparation time _____

Difficulty Scale 1 2 3 4 5 Cooking time _____

Ingredients

Name   Weight/Measure/Amount

------------------------------   ------------------------------
------------------------------   ------------------------------
------------------------------   ------------------------------
------------------------------   ------------------------------
------------------------------   ------------------------------
------------------------------   ------------------------------
------------------------------   ------------------------------

Method

Recipe

Serves _____   Preparation time _____

Difficulty Scale   [1] [2] [3] [4] [5]   Cooking time   _____

Ingredients

Name	Weight/Measure/Amount
----------------------------	----------------------------
----------------------------	----------------------------
----------------------------	----------------------------
----------------------------	----------------------------
----------------------------	----------------------------
----------------------------	----------------------------
----------------------------	----------------------------

Method

Recipe

Serves _____ Preparation time _____

Difficulty Scale 1 2 3 4 5 Cooking time _____

Ingredients

Name   Weight/Measure/Amount

----------------------------   ----------------------------

----------------------------   ----------------------------

----------------------------   ----------------------------

----------------------------   ----------------------------

----------------------------   ----------------------------

----------------------------   ----------------------------

----------------------------   ----------------------------

Method

Recipe ....

Serves _____ Preparation time _____

Difficulty Scale | 1 | 2 | 3 | 4 | 5 | Cooking time _____

Ingredients

Name   Weight/Measure/Amount

-----------------------------------   -----------------------------------

-----------------------------------   -----------------------------------

-----------------------------------   -----------------------------------

-----------------------------------   -----------------------------------

-----------------------------------   -----------------------------------

-----------------------------------   -----------------------------------

-----------------------------------   -----------------------------------

Method

Recipe

Serves _____ Preparation time _____

Difficulty Scale | 1 | 2 | 3 | 4 | 5 | Cooking time _____

Ingredients

Name   Weight/Measure/Amount

------------------------------------   ------------------------------------

------------------------------------   ------------------------------------

------------------------------------   ------------------------------------

------------------------------------   ------------------------------------

------------------------------------   ------------------------------------

------------------------------------   ------------------------------------

------------------------------------   ------------------------------------

Method

Recipe

Serves _____ Preparation time _____

Difficulty Scale | 1 | 2 | 3 | 4 | 5 | Cooking time _____

Ingredients

Name	Weight/Measure/Amount
-------------------------------	-------------------------------
-------------------------------	-------------------------------
-------------------------------	-------------------------------
-------------------------------	-------------------------------
-------------------------------	-------------------------------
-------------------------------	-------------------------------
-------------------------------	-------------------------------

Method

Recipe

Serves _____ Preparation time _____

Difficulty Scale [1] [2] [3] [4] [5]   Cooking time _____

Ingredients

Name   Weight/Measure/Amount

----------------------------- -----------------------------

----------------------------- -----------------------------

----------------------------- -----------------------------

----------------------------- -----------------------------

----------------------------- -----------------------------

----------------------------- -----------------------------

----------------------------- -----------------------------

Method

Recipe --

Serves _____ Preparation time _____

Difficulty Scale [1][2][3][4][5] Cooking time _____

Ingredients

Name	Weight/Measure/Amount
-------------------------------	-------------------------------
-------------------------------	-------------------------------
-------------------------------	-------------------------------
-------------------------------	-------------------------------
-------------------------------	-------------------------------
-------------------------------	-------------------------------
-------------------------------	-------------------------------

Method

Recipe ---

Serves _____ Preparation time _____

Difficulty Scale | 1 | 2 | 3 | 4 | 5 | Cooking time _____

Ingredients

Name   Weight/Measure/Amount

-------------------------------   -------------------------------------

-------------------------------   -------------------------------------

-------------------------------   -------------------------------------

-------------------------------   -------------------------------------

-------------------------------   -------------------------------------

-------------------------------   -------------------------------------

Method

Recipe

_____

Serves _____ Preparation time _____

Difficulty Scale | 1 | 2 | 3 | 4 | 5 | Cooking time _____

Ingredients

Name   Weight/Measure/Amount

-------------------------------------   -------------------------------------

-------------------------------------   -------------------------------------

-------------------------------------   -------------------------------------

-------------------------------------   -------------------------------------

-------------------------------------   -------------------------------------

-------------------------------------   -------------------------------------

-------------------------------------   -------------------------------------

Method

Recipe

Serves _____   Preparation time _____

Difficulty Scale | 1 | 2 | 3 | 4 | 5 | Cooking time   _____

Ingredients

Name	Weight/Measure/Amount
----------------------------------	----------------------------------
----------------------------------	----------------------------------
----------------------------------	----------------------------------
----------------------------------	----------------------------------
----------------------------------	----------------------------------
----------------------------------	----------------------------------
----------------------------------	----------------------------------

Method

Recipe

Serves _____ Preparation time _____

Difficulty Scale [1 | 2 | 3 | 4 | 5] Cooking time _____

Ingredients

Name	Weight/Measure/Amount

Method

Recipe --

Serves _____   Preparation time _____

Difficulty Scale   [1] [2] [3] [4] [5]   Cooking time   _____

Ingredients

Name   Weight/Measure/Amount

------------------------------------   ------------------------------------
------------------------------------   ------------------------------------
------------------------------------   ------------------------------------
------------------------------------   ------------------------------------
------------------------------------   ------------------------------------
------------------------------------   ------------------------------------
------------------------------------   ------------------------------------

Method

Recipe ....

Serves _____ Preparation time _____

Difficulty Scale | 1 | 2 | 3 | 4 | 5 | Cooking time _____

Ingredients

Name   Weight/Measure/Amount

-----------------------------------   -----------------------------------
-----------------------------------   -----------------------------------
-----------------------------------   -----------------------------------
-----------------------------------   -----------------------------------
-----------------------------------   -----------------------------------
-----------------------------------   -----------------------------------
-----------------------------------   -----------------------------------

Method

----

place recipes here

place recipes here

place recipes here

place recipes here

cakes, bakes and breads

Recipe ---

Serves _____ Preparation time _____

Difficulty Scale [1][2][3][4][5] Cooking time _____

Ingredients

Name   Weight/Measure/Amount

------------------------------------   ------------------------------------

------------------------------------   ------------------------------------

------------------------------------   ------------------------------------

------------------------------------   ------------------------------------

------------------------------------   ------------------------------------

------------------------------------   ------------------------------------

------------------------------------   ------------------------------------

Method

Recipe

Serves _____ Preparation time _____

Difficulty Scale [1] [2] [3] [4] [5]   Cooking time _____

Ingredients

Name   Weight/Measure/Amount

-------------------------------------   -------------------------------------

-------------------------------------   -------------------------------------

-------------------------------------   -------------------------------------

-------------------------------------   -------------------------------------

-------------------------------------   -------------------------------------

-------------------------------------   -------------------------------------

-------------------------------------   -------------------------------------

Method

Recipe

Serves _____ Preparation time _____

Difficulty Scale [1] [2] [3] [4] [5] Cooking time _____

Ingredients

Name	Weight/Measure/Amount
------------------------------------	------------------------------------
------------------------------------	------------------------------------
------------------------------------	------------------------------------
------------------------------------	------------------------------------
------------------------------------	------------------------------------
------------------------------------	------------------------------------
------------------------------------	------------------------------------

Method

Recipe ....

Serves _____ Preparation time _____

Difficulty Scale [1|2|3|4|5] Cooking time _____

Ingredients

Name	Weight/Measure/Amount
-------------------------------	-------------------------------
-------------------------------	-------------------------------
-------------------------------	-------------------------------
-------------------------------	-------------------------------
-------------------------------	-------------------------------
-------------------------------	-------------------------------
-------------------------------	-------------------------------

Method

....
....
....
....
....
....
....

Recipe --

Serves _____ Preparation time _____

Difficulty Scale [1][2][3][4][5] Cooking time _____

==

Ingredients

Name   Weight/Measure/Amount

---------------------------------- ----------------------------------

---------------------------------- ----------------------------------

---------------------------------- ----------------------------------

---------------------------------- ----------------------------------

---------------------------------- ----------------------------------

---------------------------------- ----------------------------------

---------------------------------- ----------------------------------

==

Method

Recipe --

Serves _____ Preparation time _____

Difficulty Scale | 1 | 2 | 3 | 4 | 5 | Cooking time _____

Ingredients

Name	Weight/Measure/Amount
----------------------------------	----------------------------------
----------------------------------	----------------------------------
----------------------------------	----------------------------------
----------------------------------	----------------------------------
----------------------------------	----------------------------------
----------------------------------	----------------------------------
----------------------------------	----------------------------------

Method

Recipe

Serves _____ Preparation time _____

Difficulty Scale [1] [2] [3] [4] [5] Cooking time _____

Ingredients

Name   Weight/Measure/Amount

---------------------------------   ---------------------------------

---------------------------------   ---------------------------------

---------------------------------   ---------------------------------

---------------------------------   ---------------------------------

---------------------------------   ---------------------------------

---------------------------------   ---------------------------------

---------------------------------   ---------------------------------

Method

Recipe --

Serves _____ Preparation time _____

Difficulty Scale [1] [2] [3] [4] [5] Cooking time _____

Ingredients

Name   Weight/Measure/Amount

---------------------------------   ---------------------------------

---------------------------------   ---------------------------------

---------------------------------   ---------------------------------

---------------------------------   ---------------------------------

---------------------------------   ---------------------------------

---------------------------------   ---------------------------------

---------------------------------   ---------------------------------

Method

Recipe --

Serves _____ Preparation time _____

Difficulty Scale | 1 | 2 | 3 | 4 | 5 | Cooking time   _____

Ingredients

Name   Weight/Measure/Amount

------------------------------------   ------------------------------------

------------------------------------   ------------------------------------

------------------------------------   ------------------------------------

------------------------------------   ------------------------------------

------------------------------------   ------------------------------------

------------------------------------   ------------------------------------

------------------------------------   ------------------------------------

Method

Recipe

Serves _____ Preparation time _____

Difficulty Scale | 1 | 2 | 3 | 4 | 5 | Cooking time _____

Ingredients

Name   Weight/Measure/Amount

------------------------------   ------------------------------

------------------------------   ------------------------------

------------------------------   ------------------------------

------------------------------   ------------------------------

------------------------------   ------------------------------

------------------------------   ------------------------------

------------------------------   ------------------------------

Method

Recipe

Serves _____ Preparation time _____

Difficulty Scale [1] [2] [3] [4] [5]   Cooking time _____

Ingredients

Name   Weight/Measure/Amount

------------------------------------ ------------------------------------
------------------------------------ ------------------------------------
------------------------------------ ------------------------------------
------------------------------------ ------------------------------------
------------------------------------ ------------------------------------
------------------------------------ ------------------------------------
------------------------------------ ------------------------------------

Method

Recipe --

Serves _____   Preparation time _____

Difficulty Scale | 1 | 2 | 3 | 4 | 5 | Cooking time _____

Ingredients

Name   Weight/Measure/Amount

------------------------------------   ------------------------------------

------------------------------------   ------------------------------------

------------------------------------   ------------------------------------

------------------------------------   ------------------------------------

------------------------------------   ------------------------------------

------------------------------------   ------------------------------------

------------------------------------   ------------------------------------

Method

Recipe --

Serves _____ Preparation time _____

Difficulty Scale | 1 | 2 | 3 | 4 | 5 | Cooking time _____

Ingredients

Name	Weight/Measure/Amount
-------------------------------	-------------------------------
-------------------------------	-------------------------------
-------------------------------	-------------------------------
-------------------------------	-------------------------------
-------------------------------	-------------------------------
-------------------------------	-------------------------------
-------------------------------	-------------------------------

Method

Recipe ....

Serves _____ Preparation time _____

Difficulty Scale | 1 | 2 | 3 | 4 | 5 | Cooking time _____

Ingredients

Name	Weight/Measure/Amount
----------------------------------	----------------------------------
----------------------------------	----------------------------------
----------------------------------	----------------------------------
----------------------------------	----------------------------------
----------------------------------	----------------------------------
----------------------------------	----------------------------------
----------------------------------	----------------------------------

Method

----

place recipes here

place recipes here

place recipes here

place recipes here

smoothies and juices

Recipe

Serves _____   Preparation time _____

Difficulty Scale | 1 | 2 | 3 | 4 | 5 | Cooking time _____

Ingredients

Name	Weight/Measure/Amount

Method

Recipe --

Serves _____ Preparation time _____

Difficulty Scale [1] [2] [3] [4] [5]   Cooking time _____

Ingredients

Name   Weight/Measure/Amount

------------------------------------   ------------------------------------

------------------------------------   ------------------------------------

------------------------------------   ------------------------------------

------------------------------------   ------------------------------------

------------------------------------   ------------------------------------

------------------------------------   ------------------------------------

------------------------------------   ------------------------------------

Method

Recipe --

Serves _____ Preparation time _____

Difficulty Scale | 1 | 2 | 3 | 4 | 5 | Cooking time   _____

Ingredients

Name   Weight/Measure/Amount

-------------------------------   -------------------------------

-------------------------------   -------------------------------

-------------------------------   -------------------------------

-------------------------------   -------------------------------

-------------------------------   -------------------------------

-------------------------------   -------------------------------

-------------------------------   -------------------------------

Method

Recipe --

Serves _____ Preparation time _____

Difficulty Scale | 1 | 2 | 3 | 4 | 5 | Cooking time _____

Ingredients

Name   Weight/Measure/Amount

-----------------------------   -----------------------------

-----------------------------   -----------------------------

-----------------------------   -----------------------------

-----------------------------   -----------------------------

-----------------------------   -----------------------------

-----------------------------   -----------------------------

-----------------------------   -----------------------------

Method

Recipe --

Serves _____ Preparation time _____

Difficulty Scale | 1 | 2 | 3 | 4 | 5 | Cooking time _____

Ingredients

Name   Weight/Measure/Amount

-----------------------------------   -----------------------------------
-----------------------------------   -----------------------------------
-----------------------------------   -----------------------------------
-----------------------------------   -----------------------------------
-----------------------------------   -----------------------------------
-----------------------------------   -----------------------------------
-----------------------------------   -----------------------------------

Method

Recipe --

Serves _____ Preparation time _____

Difficulty Scale | 1 | 2 | 3 | 4 | 5 | Cooking time _____

Ingredients

Name	Weight/Measure/Amount
-------------------------------	-------------------------------
-------------------------------	-------------------------------
-------------------------------	-------------------------------
-------------------------------	-------------------------------
-------------------------------	-------------------------------
-------------------------------	-------------------------------
-------------------------------	-------------------------------

Method

Recipe ---

Serves _____ Preparation time _____

Difficulty Scale | 1 | 2 | 3 | 4 | 5 | Cooking time _____

Ingredients

Name   Weight/Measure/Amount

-----------------------------------   -----------------------------------

-----------------------------------   -----------------------------------

-----------------------------------   -----------------------------------

-----------------------------------   -----------------------------------

-----------------------------------   -----------------------------------

-----------------------------------   -----------------------------------

-----------------------------------   -----------------------------------

Method

Recipe --

Serves _____ Preparation time _____

Difficulty Scale   [1] [2] [3] [4] [5]   Cooking time   _____

Ingredients

Name   Weight/Measure/Amount

----------------------------------   ----------------------------------

----------------------------------   ----------------------------------

----------------------------------   ----------------------------------

----------------------------------   ----------------------------------

----------------------------------   ----------------------------------

----------------------------------   ----------------------------------

----------------------------------   ----------------------------------

Method

Recipe --

Serves _____ Preparation time _____

Difficulty Scale [1][2][3][4][5] Cooking time _____

Ingredients

Name   Weight/Measure/Amount

------------------------------   ------------------------------

------------------------------   ------------------------------

------------------------------   ------------------------------

------------------------------   ------------------------------

------------------------------   ------------------------------

------------------------------   ------------------------------

Method

Recipe ....

Serves _____ Preparation time _____

Difficulty Scale | 1 | 2 | 3 | 4 | 5 | Cooking time _____

Ingredients

Name   Weight/Measure/Amount

------------------------------------   ------------------------------------

------------------------------------   ------------------------------------

------------------------------------   ------------------------------------

------------------------------------   ------------------------------------

------------------------------------   ------------------------------------

------------------------------------   ------------------------------------

------------------------------------   ------------------------------------

Method

----

place recipes here

place recipes here

place recipes here

place recipes here

special occasion menus

Starter --

Main Course --

Dessert --

Serves _____ Preparation time _____

Difficulty Scale | 1 | 2 | 3 | 4 | 5 | Cooking time _____

Ingredients

Name   Weight/Measure/Amount

------------------------------------   ------------------------------------

------------------------------------   ------------------------------------

------------------------------------   ------------------------------------

------------------------------------   ------------------------------------

------------------------------------   ------------------------------------

------------------------------------   ------------------------------------

------------------------------------   ------------------------------------

------------------------------------   ------------------------------------

------------------------------------   ------------------------------------

------------------------------------   ------------------------------------

------------------------------------   ------------------------------------

------------------------------------   ------------------------------------

------------------------------------   ------------------------------------

Method

Starter --

Main Course --

Dessert --

Serves _____ Preparation time _____

Difficulty Scale [1] [2] [3] [4] [5]   Cooking time _____

Ingredients

Name	Weight/Measure/Amount
------------------------------	------------------------------
------------------------------	------------------------------
------------------------------	------------------------------
------------------------------	------------------------------
------------------------------	------------------------------
------------------------------	------------------------------
------------------------------	------------------------------
------------------------------	------------------------------
------------------------------	------------------------------
------------------------------	------------------------------
------------------------------	------------------------------
------------------------------	------------------------------
------------------------------	------------------------------
------------------------------	------------------------------

Method

Starter ---

Main Course --

Dessert ---

Serves _____ Preparation time _____

Difficulty Scale | 1 | 2 | 3 | 4 | 5 | Cooking time _____

Ingredients

Name	Weight/Measure/Amount
-----------------------------	-----------------------------
-----------------------------	-----------------------------
-----------------------------	-----------------------------
-----------------------------	-----------------------------
-----------------------------	-----------------------------
-----------------------------	-----------------------------
-----------------------------	-----------------------------
-----------------------------	-----------------------------
-----------------------------	-----------------------------
-----------------------------	-----------------------------
-----------------------------	-----------------------------
-----------------------------	-----------------------------
-----------------------------	-----------------------------
-----------------------------	-----------------------------

Method